AN APOLOGY FOR THE LIFE OF MRS. SHAMELA ANDREWS

THE MINORITY PAMPHLETS.

AN APOLOGY FOR THE LIFE OF MRS. SHAMELA ANDREWS

ATTRIBUTED TO

HENRY FIELDING

WITH AN INTRODUCTION
BY
BRIAN W. DOWNS

THE FOLCROFT PRESS, INC.
FOLCROFT, PA.

First Published 1930

Reprinted 1969

AN APOLOGY FOR THE LIFE OF
MRS. SHAMELA ANDREWS

ATTRIBUTED TO
HENRY FIELDING
ℨ

WITH AN INTRODUCTION
BY
BRIAN W. DOWNS

THE
MINORITY
PRESS

AT
CAMBRIDGE
ENG.

**Gordon Fraser at St. John's College
Cambridge
1930**

MINORITY REPRINT No.

First published November 1930.

PRINTED IN ENGLAND

INTRODUCTION

I.

THE original title-page of *Shamela* clearly indicates its main purpose: the refutation and correction of " the many notorious Falshoods and Misrepresentations of a book called *Pamela*," the first, hugely successful novel of Samuel Richardson, which he had anonymously published late in 1740, pretending merely to edit authentic papers written by the chief party. For the full understanding and enjoyment of *Shamela* some familiarity with *Pamela* is required—of the original two volumes, that is to say, which were supplemented by two more on *Pamela in her Exalted Condition* early in 1742, ten months after the appearance of *Shamela*.

Pamela Andrews, then, is the daughter of poor and honest parents, and in domestic service at a large house in Bedfordshire. Upon the death of her mistress she finds herself, so her collected letters and journal disclose, exposed to the licentious advances of that lady's son and heir, Mr. B——. He employs the obvious means, cajolery and even a clumsy attempt at force, to gain his point, but her chastity and piety, reinforced by the aid of Mrs. Jervis, the housekeeper, foil him; so he decides to send her home. But the travelling chariot that is to carry her away is ordered to Mr. B——'s second country seat, in Lincolnshire. There a housekeeper of quite another stamp, the ugly and heartless Mrs. Jewkes, is in charge, and her ill-treatment all but drives the heroine, who is virtually kept a prisoner, to drown herself in the garden pond. But she finds another human ally in the ineffective curate, Mr. Williams, and when, after a little, Mr. B—— comes down to renew his attempts, he finds her as sturdy and unmanageable as before. He tries rape, he holds out a handsome settlement, he toys with the idea of a mock marriage, he even risks total separation from his charmer of fifteen; all in vain. The attraction is too great; moreover, is most surprisingly reciprocated. Pamela returns to B—— Hall and, in due form, becomes the lawless libertine's wife.

This brief sketch will make it clear to those who have also read *Shamela* what its author's "method" was, by which he proposed to discredit *Pamela*: he left the outlines of Richardson's story intact, but he substituted new personalities, new motives and self-revelatory letters for the old. The common foundations bear his superstructure as easily as the other one; this superstructure accords in design much more nearly with human nature as the satirist apprehends it; therefore it is more "probable"; and the final inference is that the postulated "editor" of *Pamela* is a sanctimonious gull, who knows nothing of the world. The morality he lets loose upon the public becomes then as suspect as his material veracity and psychology. The point is driven home by the two "covering letters" of Parson Oliver.

Other things than the morality and psychology of *Pamela* are aimed at as well. One of them is a technical matter: Pamela, the young, hardly educated servant girl, is represented as keeping up an enormous correspondence and diary; not only that, but also persevering with them in extremely unlikely circumstances, with a determination that recalls Flaubert's valiance in literary matters. Such improbability (even more glaring in certain parts of Richardson's next book than in *Pamela*) will be found directly criticised in the passage of Letter VI: "Mrs. Jervis and I are just in Bed, and the Door locked. . . . You see I write in the present Tense, as Parson Williams says." An equally obvious shaft is launched at the encomiums which Richardson saw fit to print at the head of the second edition of *Pamela*, but later withdrew. For these the author of *Shamela* substituted the letters entitled "The Editor to Himself" and "John Puff, Esq.; to the Editor."

To return to the title-page of *Shamela*: it betrays that more was aimed at than *Pamela*. There is "Mr. Conny Keyber" to account for. "Keyber" stands for Cibber, Colley Cibber, the actor, playwright and poet laureate, who had written the second book of the year 1740 with *An Apology for the Life of Mr. Colley Cibber, Comedian, Written by Himself.* The identification is quite clear from the similarity of the titles ; moreover, it had been made eleven years earlier in a play called *The Author's Farce* where "Mr Keyber" is alluded to as one of the big-wigs to whom the playwright Luckless had submitted (or tried to submit) a manuscript. But the Christian name of "Conny" is a novelty and, though near enough to Colley, seems rather meant for an allusion to Dr. Conyers Middleton, University Librarian at Cambridge, who published a *Life of Cicero* early in 1741. Middleton prefaced his biography with an Epistle Dedicatory to his patron, John, Lord Hervey, the fulsome servility of which afforded delicious opportunities to a parodist. A couple of parallel passages will suffice to prove that it is Conyers Middleton who was glanced at :

> Middleton : " I cannot forebear boasting, that some parts of my present work have been brightened by the strokes of Your Lordship's pencil." (v).

> Dedication to *Shamela*: "First, then, Madam, I must tell the World, that you have tickled up and brightned many Strokes of this Work by your Pencil." (vii).

and

> Middleton : " That singular temperance in diet, in which Your Lordship perseveres." (viii).

> *Shamela* : " *Fourthly*, you have a Virtue . . . forebearing to over-eat yourself, and this in spite of all the luscious Temptations of Puddings and Custards." (ix).

The Dedication of *Shamela* ridicules, in the Reverend T. Dampier's contemporary opinion, " very justly and prettily " Middleton's panegyrics upon Lord Hervey and, that done, the anonymous author could drop his interest in the *Life of Cicero*, which may have some connection with one of the other two butts in the fact that Cibber himself was meditating a *Character and Conduct of Cicero* and indulged in a " more than *Ciceronian eloquence*," which Parson Oliver finds distasteful, but for which Middleton was much admired. The association of Cibber's auto-biography with Richardson's novel, however, remains something of a puzzle, which the text of *Shamela* and outside evidence do very little to elucidate. It is just possible that, in her replies, Mrs. Henrietta Maria Honora Andrews was originally planned to communicate stage gossip in Cibber's language to her daughter who longed so " *to be in the Balconey at the Old House* " near which her mother lodged and where she had once sold oranges, but, if that was the author's first design, he carried it no further than the end of the first letter. It is more probable that the author of *Shamela* believed Colley Cibber responsible for *Pamela* and, by and large, to have sentimentalised and sham-moralised the novel therewith, as a lifetime before he had sentimentalised and attempted to sham-moralise the Restoration comedy with *Love's Last Shift*. The imaginary Parson Oliver certainly seems to believe it when he refers to the "Composer's" " excellent Knack of making each Character amiable, which he lays his hands on," which hits off Cibber and his *Apology* pretty well.

Curiously enough, Cibber's *Apology* comes in for some satirical knocks in another work of fiction whose main aim was to criticise the ethics of *Pamela* and " show a better way " : I refer to Fielding's *Joseph Andrews*.* The passage, in the first chapter, where he brings the two books together and indicates (very speciously) his justification for doing so, is worth quoting:

" But I pass by these and many others to mention two books lately published, which represent an admirable pattern of the amiable in either sex. The former of these, which deals in male virtue, was written by the great person himself, who lived the life he hath recorded,

* In which (Bk. III, ch. vi) there is also a slighting allusion to the *Life of Cicero*.

and is by many thought to have lived such a life only in order to write it. The other is communicated to us by an historian who borrows his lights, as the common method is, from authentic papers and records. The reader, I believe, already conjectures, I mean the lives of Mr. Colley Cibber and Mrs. Pamela Andrews. . . . What the female readers are taught by the memoirs of Mrs. Andrews is so well set forth in the excellent essays or letters prefixed to the second and subsequent editions of that work, that it would be here a needless repetition. The authentic history with which I now present the public is an instance of the great good that book is likely to do, and of the prevalence of example which I have just observed : since it will appear that it was by keeping that excellent pattern of his sister's virtues before his eyes, that Mr. Joseph Andrews was chiefly enabled to preserve his purity in the midst of such great temptations. I shall only add that this character of male chastity, though doubtless as desirable and becoming in one part of the human species as in the other, is almost the only virtue which the great apologist hath not given himself for the sake of giving the example to his reader."

The last sentence, by the way, though strictly true, has given rise to misconceptions in many who have never read Cibber himself : they mistakenly think that he holds himself up as a terrible rake, whereas, as a matter of fact, he hardly touches on his private life at all.

II.

The question now arises, did the same armourer fashion these two double-barrelled guns of such similar design and aim? Was Fielding the author also of *Shamela?*

No conclusive answer can be returned to such a question ; we can merely balance the probabilities. On the one hand there is the unlikelihood that a man of sense and genius would return to a subject or combination of subjects with which he had dealt so faithfully. Against this there is a great deal more to set :—First, the fact that *Pamela* had *not* been discredited ; Fielding's renewed and persistent wrath against Cibber for the attack upon him in the *Apology* as a " broken wit " who knew " that, as he was in haste to get money, it would take up less time to be intrepidly abusive than decently entertaining ; that to draw the mob after him, he must rake the channel and pelt their superiors, etc. etc." ; then, analogies in language, such as, most obviously, the use of " doth " and " hath " and the Quicklyisms of the heroine and her mother in *Shamela*, which are repeated by Mrs. Slipslop in *Joseph Andrews* ; the expansion of Richardson's Mr. B—— into Mr. Booby in both books ; the names of the two corresponding parsons in *Shamela*, Tickletext (a parallel to the names of Puzzletext in Fielding's *Grub Street Opera* and of Murdertext in that very *Author's Farce* of Fielding's in which "Keyber" was first invented) and Oliver (who has the same name as one of Fielding's own tutors); the detestation of canting and sacerdotalism as against practical piety and honest living which colours all Fielding's mature work and accounts for the prominence given to Williams in *Shamela* ; the resemblance between the title page of *Shamela* and the phraseology with which Fielding first advertised *Jonathan Wild**: ". . . the history of that truly renowned person, Jonathan Wyld, Esq.; in which not only his Character, but that of divers other great Personages of his Time, will be set in a *just and true Light*."

In addition, there is a little external evidence. In that letter of Dampier's† in which he approved of the ridicule cast upon Middleton's Epistle Dedicatory its author is definitely set down as Fielding. Best of all, Richardson believed him to be so, though Sarah Fielding and her sisters must have had ample opportunities of disabusing his mind, if there had been grounds for doing so : in an undated letter to Lady Bradshaigh (which she answered on 16th December, 1749) he wrote that " the Pamela, which he abused in his

---

* *Daily Post*, 5 June 1742 ; italics not in the original.

† *Cit.* Cross, W. L., *The History of Henry Fielding* I (New Haven, 1918), 306.

Shamela, taught him to write to please, . . . before his Joseph Andrews (hints and names taken from that story, with a lewd and ungenerous engraftment) the poor man wrote without being read . . . ."* Lastly, Fielding framed the public denial of certain anonymous writings that had been fathered upon him in such a way as would exclude *Shamela*.

III.

We may take it, then, that *Shamela* is Fielding's. Whether or no, it is a thorough handling by the acutest mind that has concerned itself with it of the work from which, by one line or another, the myriad domestic novels of England and the world at large trace their descent. It is undeniably gross, very gross. But its frankness does what nothing else could do so effectively : it reveals to the dullest apprehension the moral insufficiency and dangers, not merely of *Pamela*, with its passing vogue, but also of all literature which proceeds to a description and interpretation of real life from ethical or religious preconceptions.

If it be accepted as Fielding's, it provides the best available portrait of one of the greatest and most lovable Englishmen in a dishabille all the more acceptable as many find the ceremoniousness of his novels, his ruffles, his bows and his Augustan talk, a trifle chilling. On these two grounds, if on no others, *Shamela* is well worth reprinting for general circulation— for the first time since the year of its original issue.

BRIAN W. DOWNS.

* *Correspondence of Samuel Richardson*, ed. Barbauld, A. L., IV. (London, 1804), 286.

AN APOLOGY FOR THE LIFE OF MRS. SHAMELA ANDREWS

In which the many notorious FALSHOODS and
MISREPRESENTATIONS of a Book called

PAMELA

are exposed and refuted; and all the matchless
ARTS of that young Politician set in a true and
just light. Together with a full Account of
all that passed between her and Parson *Arthur
Williams*; whose Character is represented in a
manner something different from that which
he bears in *PAMELA*. The whole being exact
Copies of authentick Papers delivered to the
Editor.

Necessary to be had in all FAMILIES.

BY

MR. CONNY KEYBER

LONDON
Printed for A. DODD, at the *Peacock*, without *Temple-bar*
M. DCC. XLI

To Miss *Fanny*, &c.

MADAM,

IT will be naturally expected, that when I write the Life of *Shamela*, I should dedicate it to some young Lady, whose Wit and Beauty might be the proper Subject of a Comparison with the Heroine of my Piece. This, those, who see I have done it in prefixing your Name to my Work, will much more confirmedly expect me to do ; and, indeed, your Character would enable me to run some Length into a Parallel, tho' you, nor any one else, are at all like the matchless *Shamela*.

You see, Madam, I have some Value for your Good-nature, when in a Dedication, which is properly a Panegyrick, I speak against, not for you ; but I remember it is a Life which I am presenting you, and why should I expose my Veracity to any Hazard in the Front of the Work, considering what I have done in the Body. Indeed, I wish it was possible to write a Dedication, and get any thing by it, without one Word of Flattery ; but since it is not, come on, and I hope to shew my Delicacy at least in the Compliments I intend to pay you.

First, then, Madam, I must tell the World, that you have tickled up and brightned many Strokes in this Work by your Pencil.

Secondly, You have intimately conversed with me, one of the greatest Wits and Scholars of my Age.

3

Thirdly, You keep very good Hours, and frequently spend an useful Day before others begin to enjoy it. This I will take my Oath on; for I am admitted to your Presence in a Morning before other People's Servants are up; when I have constantly found you reading in good Books; and if ever I have drawn you upon me, I have always felt you very heavy.

Fourthly, You have a Virtue which enables you to rise early and study hard, and that is, forbearing to over-eat yourself, and this in spite of all the luscious Temptations of Puddings and Custards, exciting the Brute (as Dr. *Woodward* calls it) to rebel. This is a Virtue which I can greatly admire, though I much question whether I could imitate it.

Fifthly, A Circumstance greatly to your Honour, that by means of your extraordinary Merit and Beauty; you was carried into the Ball-Room at the *Bath*, by the discerning Mr. *Nash*; before the Age that other Young Ladies generally arrived at that Honour, and while your Mamma herself existed in her perfect Bloom. Here you was observed in Dancing to balance your Body exactly, and to weigh every Motion with the exact and equal Measure of Time and Tune; and though you sometimes made a false Step, by leaning too much to one Side; yet every body said you would one time or other dance perfectly well, and uprightly.

Sixthly, I cannot forbear mentioning those pretty little Sonnets, and sprightly Compositions, which though they came from you with so much Ease, might be mentioned to the Praise of a great or grave Character.

And now, Madam, I have done with you; it only remains to pay my Acknowledgments to an

Author, whose Stile I have exactly followed in this
Life, it being the properest for Biography. The
Reader, I believe, easily guesses I mean *Euclid's
Elements ;* it was *Euclid* who taught me to write.
It is you, Madam, who pay me for Writing. There-
fore I am to both,

A most Obedient, and

obliged humble Servant,

CONNY KEYBER.

LETTERS TO THE EDITOR

THE EDITOR to *Himself*.

Dear SIR,

HOWEVER you came by the excellent *Shamela,*
out with it, without Fear or Favour, Dedication
and all ; believe me, it will go through many Editions,
be translated into all Languages, read in all Nations
and Ages, and to say a bold word, it will do more
good than the C——y have done harm in the World.

> *I am, Sir,*
>
> *Sincerely your Well-wisher,*
>
> Yourself.

JOHN PUFF, *Esq.*; *to the* EDITOR.

SIR,

I HAVE read your *Shamela* through and through,
and a most inimitable Performance it is. Who
is he, what is he that could write so excellent a Book ?
he must be doubtless most agreeable to the Age, and
to *his Honour* himself ; for he is able to draw every
thing to Perfection but Virtue. Whoever the Author
be, he hath one of the worst and most fashionable
Hearts in the World, and I would recommend to

him, in his next Performance, to undertake the Life of *his Honour*. For he who drew the Character of Parson *Williams*, is equal to the Task ; nay he seems to have little more to do than to pull off the Parson's Gown, and *that* which makes him so agreeable to *Shamela*, and the Cap will fit.

I am, Sir,

Your humble Servant,

JOHN PUFF.

Note, Reader, several other COMMENDATORY LETTERS and COPIES of VERSES will be prepared against the NEXT EDITION.

AN APOLOGY FOR THE LIFE OF MRS. SHAMELA ANDREWS

Parson TICKLETEXT *to Parson* OLIVER.

Rev. SIR,

HEREWITH I transmit you a Copy of sweet, dear, pretty *Pamela*, a little Book which this Winter hath produced ; of which, I make no doubt, you have already heard mention from some of your Neighbouring Clergy ; for we have made it our common Business here, not only to cry it up, but to preach it up likewise : The Pulpit, as well as the Coffee-house, hath resounded with its Praise, and it is expected shortly, that his L——p will recommend it in a —— Letter to our whole Body.

And this Example, I am confident, will be imitated by all our Cloth in the Country : For besides speaking well of a Brother, in the Character of the Reverend Mr. *Williams*, the useful and truly religious Doctrine of *Grace* is every where inculcated.

This Book is the " SOUL of *Religion*, Good-Breeding, Discretion, Good-Nature, Wit, Fancy, Fine Thought, and Morality. There is an Ease, a natural Air, a dignified Simplicity, and MEASURED FULLNESS in it, that RESEMBLING LIFE, OUT-GLOWS IT. The Author hath reconciled the *pleasing* to the *proper ;* the Thought is every where exactly cloathed by the Expression ; and becomes its Dress as *roundly* and as close as *Pamela* her Country Habit ; or *as she doth her no Habit,* when modest Beauty seeks to hide itself, by casting off the Pride of Ornament, and displays itself without any Covering;" which it frequently doth in this admirable Work, and presents Images to the Reader, which the coldest Zealot cannot read without Emotion.

For my own Part (and, I believe, I may say the same of all the Clergy of my Acquaintance) "I have done nothing but read it to others, and hear others again read it to me, ever since it came into my Hands; and I find I am like to do nothing else, for I know not how long yet to come: because if I lay the Book down *it comes after me.* When it has dwelt all Day long upon the Ear, it takes Possession all Night of the Fancy. It hath Witchcraft in every Page of it."—Oh! I feel an Emotion even while I am relating this: Methinks I see *Pamela* at this Instant, with all the Pride of Ornament cast off.

"Little Book, charming *Pamela,* get thee gone; face the World, in which thou wilt find nothing like thyself." Happy would it be for Mankind, if all other Books were burnt, that we might do nothing but read thee all Day, and dream of thee all Night. Thou alone art sufficient to teach us as much Morality as we want. Dost thou not teach us to pray, to sing Psalms, and to honour the Clergy? Are not these the whole Duty of Man? Forgive me, O Author of *Pamela,* mentioning the Name of a Book so unequal to thine: But, now I think of it, who is the Author, where is he, what is he, that hath hitherto been able to hide such an encircling, all-mastering Spirit, "he possesses every Quality that Art could have charm'd by: yet hath lent it to and concealed it in Nature. The Comprehensiveness of his Imagination must be truly prodigious! It has stretched out this diminutive mere grain of Mustard seed (a poor Girl's little, &c.,) into a Resemblance of that Heaven, which the best of good Books has compared it to."

To be Short, this Book will live to the Age of the Patriarchs, and like them will carry on the good Work many hundreds of years hence, among our Posterity, who will not HESITATE their Esteem with Restraint. If the *Romans* granted Exemptions to Men who begat a *few* children for the Republick, what Distinction (if policy and we should ever be reconciled) should we find to reward this Father of Millions, which are to owe Formation to the future Effect of his Influence.—I feel another Emotion.

As soon as you have read this yourself five or six Times over (which may possibly happen within a Week) I desire you would give it to my little God-Daughter, as a Present from me. This being the only Education we intend henceforth to give our Daughters. And pray let your Servant-Maids read it over, or read it to them. Both your self and the neighbouring Clergy, will supply yourselves for the Pulpit from the Book-sellers, as soon as the fourth Edition is published.

I am,

Sir,

Your most humble Servant,

THO. TICKLETEXT.

Parson OLIVER *to Parson* TICKLETEXT.

Rev. SIR,

I RECEIVED the Favour of yours with the inclosed Book, and really must own myself sorry, to see the Report I have heard of an epidemical Phrenzy now raging in Town, confirmed in the Person of my Friend.

If I had not known your Hand, I should, from the Sentiments and Stile of the Letter, have imagined it to have come from the Author of the famous Apology, which was sent me last Summer ; and on my reading the remarkable Paragraph of *measured Fulness, that resembling Life outglows it,* to a young Baronet, he cry'd out, C—ly C—b—r by G—. But I have since observed, that this, as well as many other Expressions in your Letter, was borrowed from those remarkable Epistles, which the Author, or the Editor hath prefixed to the second Edition which you send me of his Book.

Is it possible that you or any of your Function can be in earnest, or think the Cause of Religion, or Morality, can want such slender Support? God forbid they should. As for Honour to the Clergy, I am sorry to see them so solicitous about it ; for if worldly Honour be meant, it is what their Predecessors in the pure and primitive Age, never had or sought. Indeed the secure Satisfaction of a good Conscience, the Approbation of the Wise and Good (which never were or will be the Generality of Mankind) and the extatick Pleasure of contemplating, that their ways are acceptable to the Great Creator of the Universe, will always attend those, who really deserve these Blessings : But for worldly Honours,

they are often the Purchase of Force and Fraud, we
sometimes see them in an eminent Degree possessed
by Men, who are notorious for Luxury, Pride,
Cruelty, Treachery, and the most abandoned
Prostitution ; Wretches who are ready to invent and
and maintain Schemes repugnant to the Interest,
the Liberty, and the Happiness of Mankind, not to
supply their Necessities, or even Conveniencies, but
to pamper their Avarice and Ambition. And if
this be the Road to worldly Honours, God forbid
the Clergy should be even suspected of walking in it.

The History of *Pamela* I was acquainted with
long before I received it from you, from my Neigh-
bourhood to the Scene of Action.   Indeed I was in
hopes that young Woman would have contented
herself with the Good-fortune she hath attained ;
and rather suffered her little Arts to have been
forgotten than have revived their Remembrance,
and endeavoured by perverting and misrepresenting
Facts to be thought to deserve what she now enjoys :
for though we do not imagine her the Author of the
Narrative itself, yet we must suppose the Instructions
were given by her, as well as the Reward, to the
Composer. Who that is, though you so earnestly
require of me, I shall leave you to guess from that
Ciceronian Eloquence, with which the Work abounds ;
and that excellent Knack of making every Character
amiable, which he lays his hands on.

But before I send you some Papers relating to
this Matter, which will set *Pamela* and some others
in a very different Light, than that in which they
appear in the printed Book, I must beg leave to
make some few Remarks on the Book itself, and its
tendency, (admitting it to be a true Relation,) towards

improving Morality, or doing any good, either to the present Age, or Posterity : which when I have done, I shall, I flatter myself, stand excused from delivering it, either into the hands of my Daughter, or my Servant-Maid.

The Instruction which it conveys to Servant-Maids, is, I think, very plainly this, To look out for their Masters as sharp as they can. The Consequences of which will be, besides Neglect of their Business, and the using all manner of Means to come at Ornaments of their Persons, that if the Master is not a Fool, they will be debauched by him ; and if he is a Fool, they will marry him. Neither of which, I apprehend, my good Friend, we desire should be the Case of our Sons.

And notwithstanding our Author's Professions of Modesty, which in my Youth I have heard at the Beginning of an Epilogue, I cannot agree that my Daughter should entertain herself with some of his Pictures ; which I do not expect to be contemplated without Emotion, unless by one of my Age and Temper, who can see the Girl lie on her Back, with one arm round Mrs. *Jewkes* and the other round the Squire, naked in Bed, with his Hand on her Breasts, &c., with as much Indifference as I read any other Page in the whole Novel. But surely this, and some other Descriptions, will not be put into the hands of his Daughter by any wise Man, though I believe it will be difficult for him to keep them from her ; especially if the Clergy in Town have cried & preached it up as you say.

But, my Friend, the whole Narrative is such a Misrepresentation of Facts, such a Perversion of Truth, as you will, I am perswaded, agree, as soon as you have perused the Papers I now inclose to you, that I hope you or some other well disposed Person, will communicate these Papers to the Publick, that this little Jade may not impose on the World, as she hath on her Master.

The true name of the Wench was SHAMELA, and not *Pamela*, as she stiles herself. Her Father had in his Youth the Misfortune to appear in no good Light at the Old-Bailey; he afterwards served in the Capacity of a Drummer in one of the *Scotch* Regiments in the *Dutch* Service; where being drummed out, he came over to *England*, and turned Informer against several Persons on the late Gin-Act; and becoming acquainted with an Hostler at an Inn, where a *Scotch* Gentleman's Horses stood, he hath at last by his Interest obtained a pretty snug Place in the *Custom-house*. Her Mother sold Oranges in the Play-house; & whether she was married to her Father or no, I never could learn.

After this short Introduction, the rest of her History will appear in the following letters, which I assure you are authentick.

LETTER I.

SHAMELA ANDREWS *to Mrs.* HENRIETTA MARIA HONORA ANDREWS *at her Lodgings at the* Fan *and* Pepper-Box *in* Drury-Lane.

Dear Mamma,

THIS comes to acquaint you, that I shall set out in the Waggon on *Monday*, desiring you to commodate me with a Ludgin, as near you as possible,

in *Coulstin's-Court,* or *Wild Street,* or somewhere
thereabouts ; pray let it be handsome, and not above
two Stories high : For Parson *Williams* hath promised
to visit me when he comes to Town, and I have
got a good many fine Cloaths of the Old Put my
Mistress's, who died a wil ago ; and I beleve Mrs.
Jervis will come along with me, for she says she
would like to keep a House somewhere about
Short's-Gardens, or towards *Queen-Street;* and if
there was convenience for a *Bannio,* she should like
it the better ; but that she will settle herself when
she comes to Town.—*O ! How I long to be in the
Balconey at the Old House*—so no more at present
from

Your affectionate Daughter,

SHAMELA.

LETTER II.

SHAMELA ANDREWS *to* HENRIETTA MARIA
HONORA ANDREWS.

Dear Mamma,

O WHAT News, since I writ my last ! the young
Squire hath been here, and as sure as a Gun
he hath taken a Fancy to me ; *Pamela,* says he,
(for so I am called here) you was a great Favourite
of your late Mistress's ; yes, an't please your Honour,
says I ; and I believe you deserved it, says he ;
thank your Honour for your good Opinion, says I ;
and then he took me by the Hand, and I pretended
to be shy : Laud, says I, Sir, I hope you don't intend

to be rude ; no, says he, my Dear, and then he kissed me, 'till he took away my Breath—and I pretended to be Angry, and to get away, and then he kissed me again, and breathed very short, and looked very silly ; and by Ill-Luck Mrs. *Jervis* came in, and had like to have spoiled Sport.—*How troublesome is such Interruption !* You shall hear now soon, for I shall not come away yet, so I rest,

Your affectionate Daughter,

SHAMELA.

LETTER III.

HENRIETTA MARIA HONORA ANDREWS *to* SHAMELA ANDREWS.

Dear Sham,

YOUR last Letter hath put me into a great hurry of Spirits, for you have a very difficult Part to act. I hope you will remember your Slip with Parson *Williams*, and not be guilty of any more such Folly. Truly, a Girl who hath once known what is what, is in the highest Degree inexcusable if she respects her *Digressions ;* but a Hint of this is sufficient. When Mrs. *Jervis* thinks of coming to Town, I believe I can procure her a good House, and fit for the Business ; so I am,

Your affectionate Mother,

HENRIETTA MARIA HONORA ANDREWS.

LETTER IV.

Shamela Andrews *to* Henrietta Maria Honora Andrews.

MARRY come up, good Madam, the Mother had never looked into the Oven for her Daughter, if she had not been there herself. I shall never have done if you upbraid me with having had a small One by *Arthur Williams,* when you yourself—but I say no more. *O ! What fine Times when the Kettle calls the Pot.* Let me do what I will, I say my Prayers as often as another, and I read in good Books, as often as I have Leisure ; and Parson *Williams* says, that will make amends.— So no more, but I rest,

Your afflicted Daughter,

S———

LETTER V.

Henrietta Maria Honora Andrews *to* Shamela Andrews.

Dear Child,

WHY will you give such way to your Passion ? How could you imagine I should be such a Simpleton, as to upbraid thee with being thy Mother's own Daughter ! When I advised you not to be guilty of Folly, I meant no more than that you should take care to be well paid before-hand, and not trust to Promises, which a Man seldom keeps, after he hath had his wicked Will. And seeing you have a rich Fool to deal with, your not making a good Market will be the more inexcusable; indeed, with such Gentlemen as Parson *Williams*, there is more to be said; for they have nothing to give, and are commonly otherwise the best Sort of Men. I am glad to hear you read good Books, pray continue so to do. I have inclosed you one of Mr. *Whitefield's* Sermons, and also the Dealings with him, and am,

Your affectionate Mother,

HENRIETTA MARIA &c.

LETTER VI.

SHAMELA ANDREWS *to* HENRIETTA MARIA HONORA ANDREWS.

O MADAM, I have strange Things to tell you! As I was reading in that charming Book about the Dealings, in comes my Master—to be sure he is a precious One. *Pamela*, says he, what Book is that, I warrant you *Rochester's* Poems.—No, forsooth, says I, as pertly as I could; Why how now Saucy Chops, Boldface, says he—Mighty pretty Words, says I, pert again;—Yes (says he) you are a d—d, impudent, stinking, cursed, confounded Jade, and and I have a great Mind to kick your A—. You, kiss —, says I. A-gad, says he, and so I will; with that he caught me in his Arms, and kissed me till he made my Face all over Fire. Now this served purely you know, to put upon the Fool for Anger. O! What precious Fools Men are! And so I flung from him in a mighty Rage, and pretended as how

I would go out at the Door; but when I came to the End of the Room, I stood still, and my Master cryed out, Hussy, Slut, Saucebox, Boldface, come hither—Yes to be sure, says I; why don't you come, says he; what should I come for, says I; if you don't come to me, I'll come to you, says he; I shan't come to you I assure you, says I. Upon which he run up, caught me in his Arms, and flung me upon a Chair, and began to offer to touch my Under-Petticoat. Sir, says I, you had better not offer to be rude; well, says he, no more I won't then; and away he went out of the Room. I was so mad to be sure I could have cry'd.

Oh what a prodigious Vexation it is to a Woman to be made a Fool of.

Mrs. *Jervis* who had been without, harkening, now came to me. She burst in to a violent Laugh the Moment she came in. Well, says she, as soon as she could speak, I have Reason to bless myself that I am an Old Woman. Ah Child! if you had known the Jolly Blades of my Age, you would not have been left in the lurch in this manner. Dear Mrs. *Jervis*, says I, don't laugh at one; and to be sure I was a little angry with her.—Come, says she, my dear Honeysuckle, I have one Game to play for you; he shall see you in Bed; he shall, my little Rose-bud, he shall see those pretty, little, white, round, panting—and offer'd to pull off my Handkerchief.—Fie, Mrs. *Jervis*, says I, you make me blush, and upon my Fackins, I believe she did: She went on thus. I know the Squire likes you, and notwithstanding the Aukwardness of his Proceeding, I am convinced he hath some hot Blood in his Veins, which will not let him rest, 'till he hath communicated some of his

Warmth to thee my little Angel; I heard him last
Night at our Door, trying if it was open, now to-night
I will take care it shall be so; I warrant that he
makes the second Trial; which if he doth, he shall
find us ready to receive him. I will at first counterfeit Sleep, and after a Swoon ; so that he will have
you naked in his Possession : and then if you are
disappointed, a Plague of all young Squires, say I.—
And so, Mrs. *Jervis*, says I, you would have me yield
myself to him, would you ; you would have me be a
second Time a Fool for nothing? Thank you for
that, Mrs. *Jervis*. For nothing! Marry forbid,
says she, you know he hath large Sums of Money,
besides abundance of fine Things ; and do you
think, when you have inflamed him, by giving his
Hand a Liberty with that charming Person ; and
that you know he may easily think he obtains against
your Will, he will not give anything to come at all—.
This will not do, Mrs. *Jervis*, answered I. I have
heard my Mamma say, (and so you know Madam,
I have) that in her Youth, Fellows have often taken
away in the Morning, what they gave over Night.
No, Mrs. *Jervis*, nothing under a regular taking into
keeping, a settled Settlement, for me, and all my
Heirs, all my whole Life-time, shall do the Business
—or else crosslegged, is the Word, faith, with *Sham*,
and then I snapt my Fingers.

Thursday Night, Twelve o'clock.

Mrs. *Jervis* and I are just in Bed, and the Door
unlocked ; if my Master should come—Ods-bobs !
I hear him just coming in at the Door. You see I
write in the present Tense, as Parson *Williams*
says. Well, he is in Bed between us, we both

shamming a Sleep, he steals his Hand into my Bosom, which I, as if in my Sleep, press close to me with mine, and then pretend to awake.—I no sooner see him, but I scream out to Mrs. *Jervis*, she feigns likewise but just to come to herself; we both begin, she to becall and I to bescratch very liberally. After having made pretty free Use of my Fingers, without any great Regard to the Parts I attack'd, I counterfeit a Swoon. Mrs. *Jervis* then cries out, O, Sir, what have you done, you have murthered poor *Pamela*: she is gone, she is gone.—

O what a Difficulty it is to keep one's Countenance, when a violent Laugh desires to burst forth.

The poor Booby frightned out of his Wits, jumped out of Bed, and, in his Shirt, sat down by my Bed-Side, pale and trembling, for the Moon shone, and I kept my Eyes wide open, and pretended to fix them in my Head. Mrs. *Jervis* apply'd Lavender Water, and Hartshorn, and this, for a full half Hour; when thinking I had carried it on long enough, and being likewise unable to continue the Sport any longer, I began by Degrees to come to my self.

The Squire who had sat all this while speechless, and was almost really in that Condition, which I feigned, the Moment he saw me give Symptoms of recovering my Senses, fell down on his Knees; and O *Pamela*, cryed he, can you forgive me, my injured Maid? by Heaven, I know not whether you are a Man or a Woman, unless by your swelling Breasts. Will you promise to forgive me: I forgive you! D—n you (says I), and d—n you says he, if you come to that. I wish I had never seen your bold Face, Saucy Sow, and so went out of the Room.

O what a silly Fellow is a bashful young Lover.

He was no sooner out of hearing, as we thought, than we both burst into a violent laugh. Well, says Mrs. *Jervis*, I never saw any thing better acted than your Part: But I wish you may not have discouraged him from any future Attempt; especially since his Passions are so cool, that you could prevent his Hands going further than your Bosom. Hang him, answer'd I, he is not quite so cold as that I assure you; our Hands on neither side, were idle in the Scuffle, nor have left us any doubt of each other as to that matter.

Friday Morning.

My Master sent for Mrs. *Jervis*, as soon as he was up, and bid her give an Account of the Plate and Linnen in her Care; and told her, he was resolved that both she and the little Gipsy (I'll assure him) should set out together. Mrs. *Jervis* made him a saucy Answer; which any Servant of Spirit, you know, would, tho' it should be one's Ruin; and came immediately in Tears to me, crying, she had lost her Place on my Account, and that she should be forced to take to a House, as I mentioned before; and that she hoped I would, at least, make her all the amends in my power, for her Loss on my Account, and come to her House whenever I was sent for. Never fear, says I, I'll warrant we are not so near being turned away, as you imagine; and, i'cod, now it comes into my Head, I have a Fetch for him, and you shall assist me in it. But it being now late, and my Letter pretty long, no more at present from

Your Dutiful Daughter,

SHAMELA.

LETTER VII.

Mrs. LUCRETIA JERVIS *to* HENRIETTA MARIA
HONORA ANDREWS.

Madam,

MISS *Sham* being set out in a Hurry for my
Master's House in *Lincolnshire,* desired me to
acquaint you with the Success of her Stratagem,
which was to dress herself in the plain Neatness of
a Farmer's Daughter, for she before wore the
Cloaths of my late Mistress, and to be introduced
by me as a Stranger to her Master. To say the
Truth, she became the Dress extremely, and if I
was to keep a House a thousand Years, I would never
desire a prettier Wench in it.

As soon as my Master saw her, he immediately
threw his Arms round her Neck, and smothered
her with Kisses (for indeed he hath but very little
to say for himself to a Woman). He swore that
Pamela was an ugly Slut, (pardon, dear Madam,
the Coarseness of the Expression) compared to such
divine Excellence. He added, he would turn
Pamela away immediately, and take this new Girl,
whom he thought to be one of his Tenant's Daughters
in her Room.

Miss *Sham* smiled at these Words, and so did
your humble Servant, which he perceiving, looked
very earnestly at your fair Daughter, and discovered
the Cheat.

How *Pamela,* says he, is it you? I thought, Sir,
said Miss, after what had happened, you would
have known me in any Dress. No, Hussy, says he,
but after what hath happened I should know thee
out of any Dress from all thy Sex. He then was

what we Women call rude, when done in the Presence of others; but it seems it is not the first time, and Miss defended herself with great Strength and Spirit.

The Squire, who thinks her a pure Virgin, and who knows nothing of my Character, resolved to send her into *Lincolnshire*, on Pretence of conveying her home; where our old Friend *Nanny Jewkes* is Housekeeper, and where Miss had her small one by Parson *Williams* about a year ago. This is a Piece of News communicated to us by *Robin* Coachman, who is intrusted by his Master to carry on this Affair privately for him: But we hang together, I believe, as well as any Family of Servants in the Nation.

You will, I believe, Madam, wonder that the Squire, who doth not want Generosity, should never have mentioned a Settlement all this while, I believe it slips his Memory: But it will not be long first, no doubt: For, as I am convinced the young Lady will do nothing unbecoming your Daughter, nor ever admit him to taste her Charms, without something sure and handsome before-hand; so, I am certain, the Squire will never rest till they have danced *Adam* and *Eve's* kissing dance together. Your Daughter set out Yesterday Morning, and told me, as soon as she arrived, you might depend on hearing from her.

Be pleased to make my Compliments acceptable to Mrs. *Davis* and Mrs. *Silvester*, and Mrs. *Jolly*, and all Friends, and permit me the Honour, Madam, to be with the utmost Sincerity,

Your most Obedient,

Humble Servant,

LUCRETIA JERVIS.

If the Squire should continue his Displeasure against me, so as to insist on the Warning he hath given me, you will see me soon, and I will lodge in the same House with you, if you have room, till I can provide for myself to my liking.

LETTER VIII.

HENRIETTA MARIA HONORA ANDREWS *to* LUCRETIA JERVIS.

Madam,

I RECEIVED the Favour of your Letter, and I find you have not forgot your usual Politeness, which you learned when you was in keeping with a Lord.

I am very much obliged to you for your Care of my Daughter, am glad to hear she hath taken such good Resolutions, and hope she will have sufficient Grace to maintain them.

All Friends are well, and remember to you. You will excuse the Shortness of this Scroll; for I have sprained my right Hand, with boxing three new-made Officers.—Tho' to my Comfort, I beat them all. I rest.

Your Friend and Servant,

HENRIETTA, &C.

LETTER IX.

Shamela Andrews *to* Henrietta Maria Honora Andrews.

Dear Mamma,

I SUPPOSE Mrs. *Jervis* acquainted you with what past 'till I left *Bedfordshire* ; whence I am after a very pleasant Journey arrived in *Lincolnshire,* with your old Acquaintance Mrs. *Jewkes,* who formerly helped Parson *Williams* to me ; and now designs I see, to sell me to my Master ; thank her for that ; she will find two Words go to that Bargain.

The Day after my Arrival here, I received a Letter from Mr. *Williams,* and as you have often desired to see one from him, I have inclosed it to you ; it is, I think, the finest I ever received from that charming Man, and full of a great deal of Learning.

O *! What a brave Thing it is to be a Schollard, and to be able to talk Latin.*

Parson *Williams to* Pamela *Andrews.*

Mrs. Pamela,

HAVING learnt by means of my Clerk, who Yesternight visited the Revd. Mr. *Peters* with my Commands, that you are returned into this County, I purposed to have saluted your fair Hands this Day towards Even : But am obliged to sojourn this Night at a neighbouring Clergyman's ; where we are to pierce a Virgin Barrel of Ale, in a Cup of which I shall not be unmindful to celebrate your Health.

I hope you have remembered your Promise, to bring me a leaden Canister of Tobacco (the Saffron

Cut) for in Troth, this Country at present affords nothing worthy the replenishing a Tube with.— Some I tasted the other Day at an Alehouse, gave me the Heart-Burn, tho' I filled no oftner than five times.

I was greatly concerned to learn, that your late Lady left you nothing, tho' I cannot say the Tidings much surprized me: For I am too intimately acquainted with the Family; (myself, Father, and Grandfather having been successive Incumbents on the same Cure, which you know is in their Gift) I say, I am too well acquainted with them to expect much from their Generosity. They are in Verity, as worthless a Family as any other whatever. The young Gentleman, I am informed, is a perfect Reprobate; that he hath an *Ingenium Versatile* to every Species of Vice, which, indeed, no one can much wonder at, who animadverts on that want of Respect to the Clergy, which was observable in him when a Child. I remember when he was at the Age of Eleven only, he met my Father without either pulling off his Hat, or riding out of the way. Indeed, a Contempt of the Clergy is the fashionable Vice of the Times; but let such Wretches know, they cannot hate, detest, and despise us, half so much as we do them.

However, I have prevailed on myself to write a civil Letter to your Master, as there is a Probability of his being shortly in a Capacity of rendring me a Piece of Service; my good Friend and Neighbour the Revd. Mr. *Squeeze-Tithe* being, as I am informed by one whom I have employed to attend for that Purpose, very near his Dissolution.

You see, sweet Mrs. *Pamela*, the Confidence with

which I dictate these Things to you; whom after those Endearments which have passed between us, I must in some Respects estimate as my Wife: For tho' the Omission of the Service was a Sin; yet, as I have told you, it was a venial One, of which I have truly repented, as I hope you have; and also that you have continued the wholesome Office of reading good Books, and are improved in your Psalmody, of which I shall have a speedy Trial: For I purpose to give you a Sermon next *Sunday*, and shall spend the Evening with you, in Pleasures, which tho' not strictly innocent, are however to be purged away by frequent and sincere Repentance. I am,

Sweet Mrs. Pamela,

Your faithful Servant,

ARTHUR WILLIAMS.

You find, Mamma, what a charming way he hath of Writing, and yet I assure you, that is not the most charming thing belonging to him: For, tho' he doth not put any Dears, and Sweets, and Loves into his Letters, yet he says a thousand of them: For he can be as fond of a Woman, as any Man living.

Sure Women are great Fools, when they prefer a laced Coat to the Clergy, whom it is our Duty to honour and respect.

Well, on *Sunday* Parson *Williams* came, according to his Promise, and an excellent Sermon he preached; his Text was, *Be not Righteous over-much;* and, indeed, he handled it in a very fine way; he shewed us that the Bible doth not require too much Goodness of us, and that People very often call things Goodness

that are not so. That to go to Church, and to pray,
and to sing Psalms, and to honour the Clergy, and
to repent, is true Religion; and 'tis not doing good
to one another, for that is one of the greatest Sins
we can commit, when we don't do it for the sake of
Religion. That those People who talk of Vartue
and Morality, are the wickedest of all Persons.
That 'tis not what we do, but what we believe, that
must save us, and a great many other good Things;
I wish I could remember them all.

As soon as Church was over, he came to the
Squire's House, and drank tea with Mrs. *Jewkes*
and me; after which Mrs. *Jewkes* went out and left
us together for an Hour and half—Oh! he is a
charming Man.

After Supper he went Home, and then Mrs.
Jewkes began to catechize me, about my Familiarity
with him. I see she wants him herself. Then she
proceeded to tell me what an Honour my Master
did me in liking me, and that it was both an inexcusable Folly and Pride in me, to pretend to refuse
him any Favour. Pray, Madam, says I, consider I
am a poor Girl, and have nothing but my Modesty
to trust to. If I part with that, what will become of
me. Methinks, says she, you are not so mighty
modest when you are with Parson *Williams*; I
have observed you gloat at one another in a manner
that hath made me blush. I assure you, I shall
let the Squire know what sort of Man he is; you may
do your Will, says I, as long as he hath a Vote for
Pallamant-Men, the Squire dares do nothing to
offend him; and you will only shew that you are
jealous of him, and that's all. How now, Mynx,
says she; Mynx! No more Mynx than yourself,

says I ; with that she hit me a Slap on the Shoulder ;
and I flew at her and scratched her Face, i' cod,
'till she went crying out of the Room ; so no more
at present, from

> *Your Dutiful Daughter,*
>
> SHAMELA.

LETTER X.

SHAMELA ANDREWS *to* HENRIETTA MARIA HONORA ANDREWS.

O MAMMA ! Rare News ! As soon as I was up
this Morning, a Letter was brought me from
the Squire, of which I send you a Copy.

Squire BOOBY *to* PAMELA.

Dear Creature,

I HOPE you are not angry with me for the Deceit
put upon you, in conveying you to *Lincolnshire,*
when you imagined yourself going to *London.*
Indeed, my dear *Pamela,* I cannot live without you ;
and will very shortly come down and convince you,
that my Designs are better than you imagine, and
such as you may with Honour comply with. I am,

> *My Dear Creature,*
>
> *Your doating Lover,*
>
> BOOBY.

Now, Mamma, what think you ?—For my own
Part, I am convinced he will marry me, and faith so
he shall. O ! Bless me ! I shall be Mrs. *Booby,*
and be Mistress of a great Estate, and have a dozen

Coaches and Six, and a fine House at *London*, and
another at *Bath*, and Servants, and Jewels, and Plate,
and go to Plays, and Operas, and Court; and do
what I will, and spend what I will. But poor
Parson *Williams*! Well! and can't I see Parson
Williams, as well after Marriage as before : For
I shall never care a Farthing for my Husband.
No, I hate and despise him of all Things.

Well, as soon as I had read my Letter, in came
Mrs. *Jewkes*. You see, Madam, says she, I carry the
Marks of your Passion about me; but I have received
order from my Master to be civil to you, and I must
obey him; for he is the best Man in the World,
notwithstanding your Treatment of him. My Treatment of him; Madam, says I? Yes, says she, your
Insensibility to the Honour he intends you, of making
you his Mistress. I would have you to know,
Madam, I would not be Mistress to the greatest
King, no nor Lord in the Universe. I value my
Vartue more than I do any thing my Master can
give me; and so we talked a full Hour and a half,
about my Vartue; and I was afraid at first, she had
heard something about the Bantling, but I find
she hath not; tho' she is as jealous, and suspicious,
as old Scratch.

In the Afternoon, I stole into the Garden to meet
Mr. *Williams*; I found him at the Place of his
Appointment, and we staid in a kind of Arbour, till
it was quite dark. He was very angry when I told
him what Mrs. *Jewkes* had threatned—Let him
refuse me the Living, says he, if he dares, I will
vote for the other Party; and not only so, but will
expose him all over the Country. I owe him 150*l.*
indeed, but I don't care for that; by that time the

Election is past, I shall be able to plead the *Statue* of *Lamentations*.

I could have stayed with the dear Man forever, but when it grew dark, he told me, he was to meet the neighbouring Clergy, to finish the Barrel of Ale they had tapped the other Day, and believed they should not part till three or four in the Morning —So he left me, and I promised to be penitent, and go on with my reading in good Books.

As soon as he was gone, I bethought myself what Excuse I should make to Mrs. *Jewkes*, and it came into my Head to pretend as how I intended to drown myself; so I stript off one of my Petticoats, and threw it into the Canal; and then I went and hid myself in the Coal-hole, where I lay all Night; and comforted myself with repeating over some Psalms, and other good things, which I had got by heart.

In the Morning Mrs. *Jewkes* and all the Servants were frighted out of their Wits, thinking I had run away; and not devising how they should answer it to their Master. They searched all the likeliest Places they could think of for me, and at last saw my Petticoat floating in the Pond. Then they got a Drag-Net, imagining I was drowned, and intending to drag me out; but at last *Moll* Cook coming for some Coals, discovered me lying all along in no very good Pickle. Bless me! Mrs. *Pamela*, says she, what can be the Meaning of this? I don't know, says I, help me up, and I will go in to Breakfast, for indeed I am very hungry. Mrs. *Jewkes* came in immediately, and was so rejoyced to find me alive, that she asked with great Good-Humour, where I had been? and how my Petticoat came into the

D

Pond. I answered, I believed the Devil had put
it into my Head to drown my self; but it was a Fib;
for I never saw the Devil in my Life, nor I don't
believe he hath any thing to do with me.

So much for this Matter. As soon as I had
breakfasted, a Coach and Six came to the Door,
and who should be in it but my Master.

I immediately run up into my Room, and stript,
and washed, and drest my self as well as I could,
and put on my prettiest round-ear'd Cap, and pulled
down my Stays, to shew as much as I could of my
Bosom, (for Parson *Williams* says, that is the most
beautiful part of a Woman) and then I practised
over all my Airs before the Glass, and then I sat
down and read a Chapter in the Whole Duty of
Man.

Then Mrs. *Jewkes* came to me and told me, my
Master wanted me below, and says she, Don't
behave like a Fool; No, thinks I to myself, I believe
I shall find Wit enough for my Master and you too.

So down goes I into the Parlour to him. *Pamela*,
says he, the Moment I came in, you see I cannot
stay long from you, which I think is a sufficient
Proof of the Violence of my Passion. Yes, Sir,
says I, I see your Honour intends to ruin me, that
nothing but the Destruction of my Vartue will
content you.

*O what a charming Word that is, rest his Soul who
first invented it.*

How can you say I should ruin you, answered the
Squire, when you shall not ask any thing which I
will not grant you. If that be true, says I, good
your Honour, let me go home to my poor but honest
Parents; that is all I have to ask, and do not ruin a

poor Maiden, who is resolved to carry her Vartue to the Grave with her.

Hussy, says he, don't provoke me, don't provoke me, I say. You are absolutely in my power, and if you won't let me lie with you by fair Means, I will by Force. O la, Sir, says I, I don't understand your paw words.—Very pretty Treatment indeed, says he, to say I use paw Words; Hussy, Gipsie, Hypocrite, Sauce-box, Boldface, get out of my Sight, or I will lend you such a Kick in the —— I don't care to repeat the Word, but he meant my hinder part. I was offering to go away, for I was half afraid, when he called me back, and took me round the Neck and kissed me, and then bid me go about my Business.

I went directly into my Room, where Mrs. *Jewkes* came to me soon afterwards. So Madam says she, you have left my Master below in a fine Pet, he hath threshed two or three of his Men already: It is mighty pretty that all his Servants are to be punished for your Impertinence.

Harkee, Madam, says I, don't you affront me, for if you do, d—n me (I am sure I have repented for using such a Word) if I am not revenged.

How sweet is Revenge : Sure the Sermon Book is in the Right, in calling it sweetest Morsel the Devil ever dropped into the Mouth of a Sinner.

Mrs. *Jewkes* remembered the Smart of my Nails too well to go farther, and so we sat down and talked about my Vartue till Dinner-time, and then I was sent for to wait on my Master. I took care to be often caught looking at him; and then I always turn'd away my Eyes, and pretended to be ashamed. As soon as the Cloth was removed, he put a Bumper

of Champagne into my Hand, and bid me drink—
O la I can't name the Health. Parson *Williams* may
well say he is a wicked Man.

Mrs. *Jewkes* took a Glass and drank the dear
Monysyllable; I don't understand that Word, but
I believe it is baudy. I then drank towards his
Honour's good Pleasure. Ay, Hussy, says he, you
can give me Pleasure if you will, Sir, says I, I shall
be always glad to do what is in my power, and so
I pretended not to know what he meant. Then he
took me in his lap.—O Mamma, I could tell you
something if I would—and he kissed me—and I said
I won't be slobbered about so, so I won't; and he
bid me get out of the Room for a saucy Baggage,
and said he had a good mind to spit in my Face.

*Sure no Man ever took such a Method to gain
a Woman's Heart.*

I had not been long in my Chamber before
Mrs. *Jewkes* came to me, and told me, my Master
would not see me any more that Evening, that is,
if he can help it; for, added she, I easily perceive
the great Ascendant you have over him; and to
confess the Truth, I don't doubt but you will shortly
be my Mistress.

What says I, dear Mrs. *Jewkes*, what do you say?
Don't flatter a poor Girl, it is impossible his Honour
can have any honourable Design upon me. And
so we talked of honourable Designs till Supper-
time. And Mrs. *Jewkes* and I supped together
upon a hot buttered Applepie; and about ten
o'Clock we went to Bed.

We had not been a Bed half an hour, when my
Master came pit a pat into the Room in his Shirt
as before, I pretended not to hear him, and Mrs.

Jewkes laid hold of one Arm, and he pulled down the Bed-cloaths and came into Bed on the other Side, and took my other Arm and laid it under him, and fell a kissing one of my Breasts as if he would have devoured it ; I was then forced to awake, and began to struggle with him, Mrs. *Jewkes* crying why don't you do it ? I have one Arm secure, if you can't deal with the rest I am sorry for you. He was as rude as possible to me ; but I remembered, Mamma, the Instructions you gave me to avoid being ravished, and followed them, which soon brought him to Terms, and he promised me, on quitting my hold, that he would leave the Bed.

O Parson Williams, *how little are all the Men in the World compared to thee.*

My Master was as good as his Word ; upon which Mrs. *Jewkes* said, O Sir, I see you know very little of our *Sect*, by parting so easily from the Blessing when you was so near it. No, Mrs. *Jewkes*, answered he, I am very glad no more hath happened, I would not have injured *Pamela* for the World. And to-morrow Morning perhaps she may hear of something to her Advantage. This she may be certain of, that I will never take her by Force, and then he left the Room.

What think you now, Mrs. *Pamela*, says Mrs. *Jewkes*, are you not yet persuaded my Master hath honourable Designs ? I think he hath given no great Proof of them to-night, said I. Your Experience I find is not great, says she, but I am convinced you will shortly be my Mistress, and then what will become of poor me.

With such sort of Discourse we both fell asleep. Next Morning early my Master sent for me, and after kissing me, gave a Paper into my hand which he bid me read; I did so, and found it to be a Proposal for settling 250*l.* a Year on me, besides several other advantagious Offers, as Presents of Money and other things. Well, *Pamela,* said he, what Answer do you make me to this. Sir, said I, I value my Vartue more than all the World, and I had rather be the poorest Man's Wife, than the richest Man's Whore. You are a Simpleton, said he; That may be, and yet I may have as much Wit as some Folks, cry'd I; meaning me, I suppose, said he; every Man knows himself best, says I. Hussy, says he, get out of the Room, and let me see your saucy Face no more, for I find I am in more Danger than you are, and therefore it shall be my Business to avoid you as much as I can; and it shall be mine, thinks I, at every turn to throw myself in your way. So I went out, and as I parted, I heard him sigh and say he was bewitched.

Mrs. *Jewkes* hath been with me since, and she assures me she is convinced I shall shortly be Mistress of the Family, and she really behaves to me, as if she already thought me so. I am resolved now to aim at it. I thought one of making a little Fortune by my Person. I now intend to make a great one by my Vartue. So asking Pardon for this long Scroll, I am,

Your dutiful Daughter,

SHAMELA.

LETTER XI.

HENRIETTA MARIA HONORA ANDREWS *to*
SHAMELA ANDREWS.

Dear Sham,

I RECEIVED your last Letter with Infinite Pleasure, and am convinced it will be your own Fault if you are not married to your Master, and I would advise you now to make no less Terms. But, my dear Child, I am afraid of one Rock only, That Parson *Williams*, I wish he was out of the Way. A Woman never commits Folly but with such Sort of Men, as by many Hints in the Letters I collect him to be : but, consider my dear Child, you will hereafter have Opportunities sufficient to indulge yourself with Parson *Williams*, or any other you like. My Advice therefore to you is, that you would avoid seeing him any more till the Knot is tied. Remember the first Lesson I taught you, that a married Woman injures only her Husband, but a single Woman herself. I am in hopes of seeing you a great Lady,

Your affectionate Mother,

HENRIETTA MARIA &c.

The following letter seems to have been written before *Shamela* received the last from her Mother.

LETTER XII.

SHAMELA ANDREWS *to* HENRIETTA MARIA HONORA ANDREWS.

Dear Mamma,

I LITTLE feared when I sent away my last that all my Hopes would be so soon frustrated; but I am certain you will blame Fortune and not me. To proceed then. About two Hours after I had left the Squire, he sent for me into the Parlour. *Pamela,* said he, and takes me gently be the hand, will you walk with me in the Garden; yes, Sir, says I, and pretended to tremble; but I hope your Honour will not be rude. Indeed, says he, you have nothing to fear from me, and I have something to tell you, which if it doth not please you, cannot offend. We walked out together, and he began thus, *Pamela,* will you tell me the Truth? Doth the Resistance you make to my Attempts proceed from Virtue only, or have I not some Rival in thy dear Bosom who might be more successful? Sir, says I, I do assure you I never had a thought of any Man in the World. How says he, not of Parson *Williams!* Parson *Williams,* says I, is the last Man upon Earth; and if I was a Dutchess, and your Honour was to make your Addresses to me, you would have no reason to be jealous of any rival, especially such a Fellow as Parson *Williams.* If ever I had a Liking, I am sure—but I am not worthy of you one Way, and no Riches should ever bribe me the other.

My dear, says he, you are worthy of every Thing, and suppose I should lay aside all Considerations of Fortune, and disregard the Censure of the World, and marry you. O Sir, says I, I am sure you can have no such Thoughts, you cannot demean yourself so low. Upon my Soul, I am in earnest, says he— O Pardon me, Sir, says I, you can't persuade me of this. How Mistress, says he, in a violent Rage, do you give me the Lie? Hussy, I have a mind to box your saucy Ears, but I am resolved I will never put it in your power to affront me again, and therefore I desire you to prepare your self for your Journey this Instant. You deserve no better Vehicle than a Cart; however, for once you shall have a Chariot, and it shall be ready for you within this half Hour; and so he flung from me in a Fury.

What a Foolish Thing it is for a Woman to dally too long with her Lover's Desires; how many have owed their being old Maids to their holding out too long.

Mrs. *Jewkes* came to me presently, and told me, I must make ready with all the Expedition imaginable, for that my Master had ordered the Chariot, and that if I was not prepared to go in it, I should be turned out of Doors, and left to find my way Home on Foot. This startled me a little, yet I resolved, whether in the right or wrong, not to submit nor ask Pardon : For that you know, Mamma, you never could your self bring me to from my Childhood : Besides, I thought he would be no more able to master his Passion for me now, than he had hitherto ; and if he sent two Horses away with me, I concluded he would send four to fetch me back. So, truly, I resolved to brazen it out, and with

all the Spirit I could muster up, I told Mrs. *Jewkes*
I was vastly pleased with the News she brought me ;
that no one ever went more readily than I should,
from a Place where my Vartue had been in continual
Danger. That as for my Master, he might easily
get those who were fit for his Purpose ; but, for my
Part, I preferred my Vartue to all Rakes whatever—
And for his Promises, and his Offers to me, I don't
value them of a Fig—Not of a Fig, Mrs. *Jewkes* ;
and then I snapt my Fingers.

Mrs. *Jewkes* went in with me, and helped me to
pack up my little All, which was soon done ; being
no more than two Day-Caps, two Night-Caps,
five Shifts, one Sham, a Hoop, a Quilted-Petticoat,
two flannel-Petticoats, two pair of Stockings, one
odd one, a pair of lac'd Shoes, a short flowered
Apron, a lac'd Neck-Handkerchief, one Clog, and
almost another, and some few Books : as, *A full
Answer is a plain and true Account*, &c., *The Whole
Duty of Man*, with only the Duty to one's Neighbour,
torn out. The Third Volume of the *Atlantis*.
Venus in the Cloyster : or, the Nun in her Smock.
*God's dealings with Mr. Whitefield. Orfus and
Eurydice.* Some Sermon Books ; and two or three
Plays, with their Titles, and Part of the first Act
torn off.

So as soon as we had put all this into a Bundle,
the Chariot was ready, and I took leave of all the
Servants, and particularly Mrs. *Jewkes*, who pretended, I believe, to be more sorry to part with
me than she was ; and then crying out with an
Air of Indifference, my Service to my Master, when
he condescends to enquire after me, I flung my self
into the Chariot, and bid *Robin* drive on.

We had not gone far, before a Man on Horseback, riding full Speed, overtook us, and coming up to the Side of the Chariot, threw a Letter into the Window, and then departed without uttering a single Syllable.

I immediately knew the Hand of my dear *Williams*, and was somewhat surprised, tho' I did not apprehend the Contents to be so terrible, as by the following exact Copy you will find them.

Parson WILLIAMS *to* PAMELA.

Dear Mrs. PAMELA,

THAT Disrespect for the Clergy, which I have formerly noted to you in that Villain your Master, hath now broke forth in a manifest Fact. I was proceeding to my Neighbour *Spruce's* Church, where I purposed to preach a Funeral Sermon, on the Death of Mr. *John Gage*, the Exciseman; when I was met by two Persons who are, it seems, Sheriffs Officers, and arrested for the 150*l*. which your Master had lent me; and unless I can find Bail within these few days, of which I see no likelihood, I shall be carried to Goal. This accounts for my not having visited you these two Days; which you might assure yourself, I should not have fail'd, if the *Potestas* had not been wanting. If you can by any means prevail on your Master to release me, I beseech you so to do, not scrupling any thing for Righteousness sake. I hear he is just arrived in this Country, I have herewith sent him a Letter, of which I transmit you a Copy. So with Prayers for your Success, I subscribe myself

Your affectionate Friend,
ARTHUR WILLIAMS.

Parson WILLIAMS *to Squire* BOOBY.

Honoured Sir,

I AM justly surprized to feel so heavy a Weight of your Displeasure, without being conscious of the least Demerit towards so good and generous a Patron, as I have ever found you : For my own Part, I can truly say,

Nil consire sibi nullæ pallescere culpæ.

And therefore, as this Proceeding is so contrary to your usual Goodness, which I have often experienced, and more especially in the Loan of this Money for which I am now arrested ; I cannot avoid thinking some malicious Persons have insinuated false Suggestions against me ; intending thereby, to eradicate those Seeds of Affection which I have hardly travailed to sowe in your Heart, and which have promised to produce such excellent Fruit. If I have any ways offended you, Sir, be graciously pleased to let me know it, and likewise to point out to me, the Means whereby I may reinstate myself in your Favour : For next to him, whom the Great themselves must bow down before, I know none to whom I shall bend with more Lowliness than your Honour. Permit me to subscribe myself,

Honoured Sir,
Your most obedient, and most obliged
And most dutiful humble Servant,
ARTHUR WILLIAMS.

The Fate of poor Mr. *Williams* shocked me more than my own : For, as the *Beggar's Opera* says, *Nothing moves one so much as a great Man in Distress.*

And to see a Man of his Learning forced to submit
so low, to one whom I have often heard him say,
he despises, is, I think, a most affecting Circumstance.
I write all this to you, Dear Mamma, at the Inn
where I lie this first night, and as I shall send it
immediately, by the Post, it will be in Town a little
before me.—Don't let my coming away vex you:
For, as my Master will be in Town in a few Days,
I shall have an Opportunity of seeing him; and
let the worst come to the worst, I shall be sure of
my Settlement at last. Which is all, from

Your dutiful Daughter,

SHAMELA.

P.S. Just as I was going to send this away a
Letter is come from my Master, desiring me to return,
with a large Number of Promises. I have him now
as sure as a Gun, as you will perceive by the Letter
itself, which I have inclosed to you.

This Letter is unhappily lost, as well as the next
which *Shamela* wrote, and which contained an account
of all the proceedings previous to her Marriage.
The only remaining one which I could preserve,
seems to have been written about a Week after the
Ceremony was perform'd, and is as follows:

SHAMELA BOOBY *to* HENRIETTA MARIA
HONORA ANDREWS.

Madam,

IN my last I left off at our sitting down to Supper
on our Wedding Night,* where I behaved with
as much Bashfulness as the purest Virgin in the World

* This was the Letter which is lost.

could have done. The most difficult Task for me
was to blush; however, by holding my Breath, and
squeezing my Cheeks with my Handkerchief, I did
pretty well. My Husband was extremely eager and
impatient to have Supper removed, after which he
gave me leave to retire into my Closet for a Quarter
of an Hour, which was very agreeable to me; for
I employed that time in writing to Mr. *Williams*,
who, as I informed you in my last, is released, and
presented to the Living, upon the Death of the
last Parson. Well, at last I went to Bed, and my
Husband soon leap'd in after me; where I shall
only assure you, that I played my Part in such a
manner, that no Bridegroom was ever better satisfied
with his Bride's Virginity. And to confess the
Truth, I might have been well enough satisfied too,
if I had never been acquainted with Parson *Williams*.

*O what regard Men who marry Widows should
have to the Qualifications of their former Husbands.*

We did not rise the next Morning till eleven, and
then we sat down to Breakfast; I eat two slices of
Bread and Butter, and drank three Dishes of Tea,
with a good deal of Sugar, and we both look'd very
silly. After Breakfast we drest ourselves, he in a
blue Camblet Coat, very richly lac'd, and Breeches
of the same; with a Paduasoy Waistcoat, laced with
Silver; and I, in one of my Mistres's Gowns. I will
have finer when I come to Town. We then took a
Walk in the Garden, and he kissed me several times,
and made me a Present of 100 Guineas, which I
gave away before Night to the Servants, twenty
to one, ten to another, and so on.

We eat a very hearty Dinner, and about eight in
the Evening went to Bed again. He is prodigiously

fond of me ; but I don't like him half as well as my dear *Williams*. The next Morning we rose earlier, and I asked him for another hundred Guineas, and he gave them me. I sent fifty to Parson *Williams*, the rest I gave away, two Guineas to a Beggar, and three to a Man riding along the Road, and the rest to other People. I long to be in *London* that I may have an Opportunity of laying some out, as well as giving away. I believe I shall buy every thing I see. What signifies having Money if one doth not spend it.

The next Day, as soon as I was up, I asked him for another Hundred. Why, my Dear, says he, I don't grudge you any thing, but how was it possible for you to lay out the other two Hundred here. La ! Sir, says I, I hope I am not obliged to give you an Account of every Shilling ; Troth, that will be being your servant still. I assure you, I married you with no such view, besides did you not tell me I should be Mistress of your Estate ? And I will be too. For tho' I brought no Fortune, I am as much your Wife as if I had brought a Million— yes, but, my Dear, says he, if you had brought a Million, you would spend it all at this rate ; besides, what will your Expenses be in *London*, if they are so great here. Truly, says I, Sir, I shall live like other Ladies of my Fashion ; and if you think, because I was a Servant, that I shall be contented to be governed as you please, I will shew you, you are mistaken. If you had not cared to marry me, you might have let it alone. I did not ask you, nor I did not court you. Madam, says he, I don't value a hundred Guineas to oblige you : but this is a Spirit which I did not expect in you, nor did I ever see any symptoms of it before. O but Times are

altered now, I am you Lady, Sir ; yes to my sorrow,
says he, I am afraid—and I am afraid to my sorrow
too : For if you begin to use me in this manner
already, I reckon you will beat me before a Month's
at an end. I am sure if you did, it would injure me
less than this barbarous Treatment ; upon which
I burst into Tears, and pretended to fall into a Fit.
This frightened him out of his wits, and he called
up the Servants. Mrs. *Jewkes* immediately came in,
and she and another of the Maids fell heartily to
rubbing my Temples, and holding Smelling-Bottles
to my Nose. Mrs. *Jewkes* told him she feared I
should never recover, upon which he began to beat
his Breasts, and cried out, O my dearest Angel, curse
on my passionate Temper, I have destroy'd her,
I have destroy'd her !—would she had spent my
whole Estate rather than that this had happened.
Speak to me, my Love, I will melt myself into Gold
for thy Pleasure. At last having pretty well tired
my self with counterfeiting, and imagining I had
continu'd long enough for my purpose in the sham
Fit, I began to move my Eyes, to loosen my Teeth,
and to open my Hands, which Mr. *Booby* no sooner
perceived than he embraced and kissed me with the
eagerest Extacy, asked my Pardon on his knees for
what I had suffered through his Folly and Perverse-
ness, and without more questions fetched me the
Money. I fancy I have effectually prevented any
farther Refusals or Inquiry into my Expences. It
would be hard indeed, that a Woman who marries a
Man only for his Money, should be debarred from
spending it.

Well, after all things were quiet, we sat down
to Breakfast, yet I resolved not to smile once, nor

to say one good-natured, or good-humoured Word on any Account.

Nothing can be more prudent in a Wife, than a sullen Backwardness to Reconciliation; it makes a Husband fearful of offending by the Length of his Punishment.

When we were drest, the Coach was by my Desire ordered for an Airing, which we took in it. A long Silence prevailed on both Sides, tho' he constantly squeezed my Hand, and kissed me, and used other Familiarities, which I peevishly permitted. At last, I opened my Mouth first.—And so, says I, you are sorry you are married;—Pray, my Dear, says he, forget what I said in a Passion. Passion, says I, is apter to discover our Thoughts than to teach us to counterfeit. Well, says he, whether you will believe me or no, I solemnly vow, I would not change thee for the richest Woman in the Universe. No, I warrant you, says I; and yet you could refuse me a nasty hundred Pound. At these very Words, I saw Mr. *Williams* riding as fast as he could across a Field; and I looked out, and saw a Lease of Greyhounds coursing a Hare, which they presently killed, and I saw him alight, and take it from them.

My Husband ordered *Robin* to drive towards him, and looked horribly out of humour, which I presently imputed to Jealousy. So I began with him first; for that is the wisest way. La, Sir, says I; what makes you look so Angry and Grim? Does the Sight of Mr. *Williams* give you all this Uneasiness? I am sure, I would never have married a Woman of whom I had so bad an Opinion, that I must be uneasy at every Fellow she looks at. My Dear, answer'd he, you injure me extremely, you was not

E

in my Thoughts, nor, indeed, could be, when they were covered by so morose a Countenance; I am justly angry with that Parson, whose Family hath been raised from the Dunghill by ours; and who hath received from me twenty kindnesses, and yet is not contented to destroy the Game in all other Places, which I freely give him leave to do; but hath the Impudence to pursue a few Hares, which I am desirous to preserve, round about this little Coppice. Look, my Dear, pray look, says he; I believe he is going to turn Higler. To confess the Truth, he had no less than three ty'd up behind his Horse, and a fourth he held in his Hand.

Pshaw, says I, I wish all the Hares in the Country were d——d (the Parson himself chid me afterwards for using the Word, tho' it was in his Service). Here's a Fuss, indeed, about a nasty little pitiful Creature, that is not half so useful as a Cat. You shall not persuade me, that a Man of your Understanding, would quarrel with a Clergyman for such a Trifle. No, no, I am the Hare, for whom poor Parson *Williams* is persecuted; and Jealousy is the Motive. If you had married one of your Quality Ladies, she would have had Lovers by dozens, she would so; but because you have taken a Servant-Maid, forsooth! you are jealous if she but looks (and then I began to Water) at a poor P—a—a—rson in his Pu—u—u—lpit, and then out burst a Flood of Tears.

My Dear, said he, for Heaven's sake dry your Eyes, and don't let him be a Witness of your Tears, which I should be sorry to think might be imputed to my Unkindness; I have already given you some Proofs that I am not jealous of this Parson; I will now give you a very strong one: For I will mount my Horse, and you shall take *Williams* into the Coach. You may be sure, this Motion pleased me, yet I pretended to make as light of it as possible, and told him, I was sorry his Behaviour had made some such glaring Instance, necessary to the perfect clearing my Character.

He soon came up to Mr. *Williams*, who had attempted to ride off, but was prevented by one of our Horsemen, whom my Husband sent to stop him. When we met, my Husband asked him how he did with a very good-humoured Air, and told him he perceived he had found good Sport this Morning. He answered pretty moderate, Sir; for that he had found the three Hares tied on to the Saddle dead in a Ditch, (winking on me at the same time) and added he was sorry there was such a Rot among them.

Well, says Mr. *Booby*, if you please, Mr. *Williams*, you shall come in and ride with my Wife. For my own part, I will mount on Horseback; for it is fine Weather, and besides, it doth not become me to loll in a Chariot, whilst a Clergyman rides on Horseback.

At which Words, Mr. *Booby* leap'd out, and Mr. *Williams* leap'd in, in an instant, telling my Husband as he mounted, he was glad to see such a Reformation, and that if he continued his Respect to the Clergy, he might assure himself of Blessings from above.

It was now that the Airing began to grow pleasant to me. Mr. *Williams*, who never had but one Fault, *viz.* that he generally smells of Tobacco, was now perfectly sweet; for he had for two Days together enjoined himself as a Penance, not to smoke till he had kissed my Lips. I will loosen you from this Obligation, says I, and observing my Husband looking another way, I gave him a charming Kiss, and then he asked me Questions concerning my Wedding-night; this actually made me blush: I vow I did not think it had been in him.

As he went along, he began to discourse very learnedly, and told me the Flesh and the Spirit were two distinct Matters, which had not the least relation to each other. That all immaterial Substances (those were his very Words) such as Love, Desire, and so forth, were guided by the Spirit. But fine Houses, large Estates, Coaches and dainty Entertainments were the Product of the Flesh. Therefore, says he, my Dear, you have two Husbands, one the object of your Love, and to satisfy your Desire; the other the Object of your Necessity, and to furnish you with those other conveniences—(I am sure I remember every Word, for he repeated it three Times; O he is very good whenever I desire him to repeat a thing to me three times he always doth it!) as then the Spirit is preferable to the Flesh, so am I preferable to your other Husband, to whom I am antecedent in Time likewise. I say these things, my Dear, (said he) to satisfie your Conscience. A Fig for my Conscience, said I, when shall I meet you again in the Garden?

My Husband now rode up to the Chariot, and asked us how we did—I hate the sight of him. Mr. *Williams* answered very well, at your Service. They then talked of the Weather, and other things, I wished him gone again, every Minute; but all in vain I had no more Opportunity of conversing with Mr. *Williams*.

Well; at Dinner Mr. *Booby* was very civil to Mr. *Williams*, and told him he was sorry for what had happened, and would make him sufficient Amends, if in his power, and desired him to accept of a note for fifty Pounds; which he was so *good* to receive, notwithstanding all that had past; and told Mr. *Booby*, he hop'd he would be forgiven, and that he would pray for him.

We make a charming Fool of him, i'fackins; Times are finely altered, I have entirely got the better of him, and am resolved never to give him his Humour.

O how foolish it is in a Woman, who hath once got the Reins into her own Hand, ever to quit them again.

After Dinner Mr. *Williams* drank the Church *et cœtera;* and smiled on me; when my Husband's Turn came, he drank *et cœtera* and the Church; for which he was very severely rebuked by Mr. *Williams;* it being a high crime, it seems, to name anything before the Church. I do not know what *Et cœtera* is, but I believe it is something concerning chusing Pallament Men; for I asked if it was not a Health to Mr. *Booby's* Borough, and Mr. *Williams* with a hearty Laugh answered, Yes, Yes, it is his Borough we mean.

I slipt out as soon as I could, hoping Mr. *Williams* would finish the Squire, as I have heard him say he could easily do, and come to me; but it happened quite otherwise, for in about half an Hour, *Booby* came to me, and told me he had left Mr. *Williams*, the Mayor of his Borough, and two or three Aldermen heartily at it, and asked me if I would go hear *Williams* sing a Catch, which, added he, he doth to a Miracle.

Every Opportunity of seeing my dear *Williams*,
was agreeable to me, which indeed I scarce had at
this time ; for when we returned, the whole Cor-
poration were got together, and the Room was in a
Cloud of Tobacco ; Parson *Williams* was at the upper
End of the Table, and he hath pure round cherry
Cheeks, and his Face looked all the World to nothing
like the Sun in a Fog. If the Sun had a Pipe in his
Mouth, there would be no Difference.

I began now to grow uneasy, apprehending I
should have no more of Mr. *Williams's* Company
that Evening, and not at all caring for my Husband,
I advised him to sit down and drink for his Country
with the rest of the Company : but he refused,
and desired me to give him some Tea, swearing
nothing would make him so sick as to hear a Parcel
of Scoundrels, roaring forth the Principles of honest
Men over their Cups, when, says he, I know most of
them are such empty Blockheads, that they don't
know their right Hand from their left ; and that
Fellow there, who hath talked so much of *Shipping*,
at the left Side of the Parson, in whom they all
place a Confidence, if I don't take care, will sell
them to my Adversary.

I don't know why I mention this stuff to you ;
for I am sure I know nothing about *Pollitricks*,
more than Parson *Williams* tells me ; who says that
the Court-side are in the right on't, and that every
Christian ought to be on the same with the Bishops.

When we had finished our Tea, we walked in
the Garden till it was dark, and then my Husband
proposed, instead of returning to the Company,
(which I desired, that I might see Parson *Williams*
again,) to sup in another Room by ourselves, which,

for fear of making him jealous, and considering too, that Parson *Williams* would be pretty far gone, I was obliged to consent to.

O! What a devilish thing it is, for a Woman to be obliged to go to bed to a spindle-shanked young Squire, she doth not like, when there is a jolly Parson in the same House she is fond of.

In the Morning I grew very peevish, and in the Dumps, notwithstanding all he could say or do to please me. I exclaimed against the Priviledge of Husbands, and vowed I would not be pulled and tumbled about. At last he hit on the only Method, which could have brought me into a Humour, and proposed to me a journey to *London*, within a few Days. This you may easily guess pleased me; for besides the Desire which I have of shewing myself forth, of buying fine Cloaths, Jewels, Coaches, Houses, and ten thousand other fine things, Parson *Williams* is, it seems, going thither too, to be *instuted*.

O! what a charming Journey I shall have; for I hope to keep the dear Man in the Chariot with me all the way; and that foolish Booby (for that is the Name Mr. Williams hath set him) will ride on horseback.

So I shall have an Opportunity of seeing you so shortly, I think I will mention no more matters to you now. O I had like to have forgot one very material thing; which is that it will look horribly, for a Lady of my Quality and Fashion, to own such a Woman as you for my Mother. Therefore we must meet in private only, and if you will never claim me, nor mention me to any one, I will always allow you what is very handsome. Parson *Williams* hath greatly advised me in this; and says, he thinks I should do very well to lay out twenty Pounds, and set you up in a little Chandler's Shop : but you must remember all my Favours to you will depend on your Secrecy ; for I am positively resolved, I will not be known to be your Daughter ; and if you tell any one so, I shall deny it with all my Might, which Parson *Williams* says, I may do with a safe conscience, being now a married Woman. So I rest

Your humble Servant,

SHAMELA.

P.S. The strangest Fancy has enter'd into my Booby's head, that can be imagined. He is resolved to have a Book made about him and me ; he proposed it to Mr. *Williams,* and offered him a Reward for his Pains ; but he says he never writ anything of that kind, but will recommend my Husband, when he comes to Town, to a Parson *who does that Sort of Business for Folks,* one who can make my Husband, and me, and Parson *Williams,* to be all great people ; for he *can make black white,* it seems. Well, but they say my Name is to be altered, Mr. *Williams,* says the first Syllabub hath too comical a Sound so it is to be changed into *Pamela;* I own I can't imagine what can be said ; for to be sure I shan't confess any of my Secrets to them, and so I whispered Parson *Williams* about that, who answered me, I need not give my self any Trouble ; for the Gentleman *who writes Lives,* never asked more than a few Names of his Customers, and that he made all the rest out of his own Head ; you mistake, Child, said he, if you apprehend any Truths are to be delivered—So far on the contrary, if you had not been acquainted with the Name, you would not have known it to be your own History. I have seen a *Piece of His Performance*, where the Person, whose Life was written, could he have risen from the Dead again, would not have even suspected he had been aimed at, unless by the Title of the Book, which was superscribed with his Name. Well, all these Matters are strange to me, and yet I can't help laughing, to think I shall see myself in a printed Book.

So much for Mrs. *Shamela* or *Pamela*, which I have taken Pains to transcribe from the Originals, sent down by her Mother in a Rage, at the Proposal in her last Letter. The Originals themselves are in my hands, and shall be communicated to you, if you think proper to make them publick; and certainly they will have their Use. The Character of *Shamela*, will make young Gentlemen wary how they take the most fatal Step both to themselves and Familes, by youthful, hasty and improper Matches; indeed, they may assure themselves, that all such Prospects of Happiness are vain and delusive, and that they sacrifice all the solid Comforts of their Lives, to a very transient Satisfaction of a Passion, which how hot soever it be, will be soon cooled; and when cooled, will afford them nothing but Repentance.

Can any thing be more miserable, than to be despised by the whole World, and that must certainly be the Consequence; to be despised by the Person obliged, which it is more than probable will be the Consequence, and of which, we see an Instance in *Shamela*; and lastly to despise one's self, which must

be the Result of any Reflection on so weak and
unworthy a Choice.

As to the Character of Parson *Williams*, I am sorry
it is a true one. Indeed those who do not know
him, will hardly believe it so; but what Scandal
doth it throw on the Order to have one bad Member,
unless they endeavour to screen and protect him?
In him you see a Picture of almost every Vice
exposed in nauseous and odious Colours; and if a
Clergyman would ask me by what Pattern he should
form himself, I would say, Be the reverse of *Williams :*
So far therefore he may be of use to the Clergy
themselves, and though God forbid there should
be many *Williams's* amongst them, you and I are
too honest to pretend, that the Body wants no
Reformation.

To say the Truth, I think no greater Instance of
the contrary can be given than that which appears
in your Letter. The confederating to cry up a
nonsensical ridiculous Book, (I believe the most
extensively so of any ever yet published,) and to be so
weak and so wicked as to pretend to make it a Matter
of Religion; whereas so far from having any moral
Tendency, the Book is by no means innocent: For,

First, There are many lascivious Images in it,
very improper to be laid before the Youth of either
Sex.

2ndly, Young Gentlemen are here taught, that to
marry their Mother's Chambermaids, and to indulge
the Passion of Lust, at the Expence of Reason and
Common Sense, is an Act of Religion, Virtue and
Honour; and, indeed, the surest Road to Happiness.

3rdly, All Chambermaids are strictly enjoined to
look out after their Masters; they are taught to use

little Arts to that purpose : and lastly, are coun-
tenanced in Impertinence to their Superiors, and
in betraying the secrets of Families.

4*thly*, In the Character of Mrs. *Jewkes* Vice is
rewarded ; whence every Housekeeper may learn the
Usefulness of pimping and bawding for her Master.

5*thly*, In Parson *Williams*, who is represented as
a faultless Character, we see a busy Fellow, inter-
meddling with the Private Affairs of his Patron,
whom he is very ungratefully forward to expose and
condemn on every Occasion.

Many more Objections might, if I had Time or
Inclination, be made to this Book ; but I apprehend,
what hath been said is sufficient to persuade you of
the use which may arise from publishing an Antidote
to this Poison. I have therefore sent you the Copies
of these Papers, and if you have Leisure to communicate them to the Press, I will transmit you the
Originals, tho' I assure you, the Copies are exact.

I shall only add, that there is not the least Founda-
tion for any thing which is said of Lady *Davers*,
or any of the other Ladies ; all that is merely to be
imputed to the Invention of the Biographer. I have
particularly enquired after Lady *Davers*, and don't
hear Mr. *Booby* hath such a Relation, or that there
is indeed any such Person existing. I am,

Dear Sir,

Most faithfully and respectfully,

Your humble Servant,

J. OLIVER.

Parson.

Parson TICKLETEXT *to Parson* OLIVER.

Dear SIR,

I HAVE read over the History of *Shamela*, as it appears in those authentic Copies you favoured me with, and am very much ashamed of the Character, which I was hastily prevailed on to give that Book. I am equally angry with the pert Jade herself, and with the Author of her Life: For I scarce know yet to whom I chiefly owe an Imposition, which hath been so general, that if Numbers could defend me from Shame, I should have no Reason to apprehend it.

As I have your implied leave to publish, what you so kindly sent me, I shall not wait for the Originals, as you assure me the Copies are exact, and as I am really impatient to do what I think a serviceable Act of Justice to the World.

Finding by the End of her last Letter, that the little Hussy was in Town, I made it pretty much my Business to enquire after her, but with no effect hitherto: As soon as I succeed in this Enquiry, you shall hear what Discoveries I can learn. You will pardon the Shortness of this Letter, as you shall be troubled with a much longer very soon: And believe me,

Dear Sir,

Your most faithful Servant,

THO. TICKLETEXT.

P.S. Since I writ, I have a certain Account, that Mr. *Booby* hath caught his Wife in bed with *Williams;* hath turned her off, and is prosecuting him in the spiritual Court.

F I N I S.

64637

FIELDING, HENRY
    AN APOLOGY FOR THE LIFE OF
MRS. SHAMELA ANDREWS.

DATE DUE
